# Moose Views

**ALASKA NORTHWEST BOOKS®**
Anchorage • Portland

I've got a few words about **ALASKA**. I've been around here longer than anybody I know, so take it from a **sourdough**.

When I
**FIRST**
came into the country,
folks were few and far between.
A guy could get

lonely.

Now it seems
I've got company

**EVERY**

weekend.

Used to be,
you
**HAD**
to
**WORK**
for a
meal.

# Now
## everybody's
### looking for a
## handout.

**Although
it is mighty
HARD
to resist
at times.**

Why, in the **OLD DAYS,** we had good, honest **COLD** that separated the cheechakos from the sourdoughs.

Anymore,
it's so warm,
you may
as well be living
in the
**TROPICS.**

**Hard to complain, though. It's still a great place to raise the little ones.**

They can go out
**trick-or-treating**
without a worry.

And the holiday lights really lift your **spirits** during winter's dark days.

Those little
**two-
leggers**
can be friendly,
too,
as long as they
stay in their
**shells.**

And when someone's in **TROUBLE,** there's always a helping hand.

Yeah,
truth be told,
this is still
a place where
**folks care**
and look out
for each other.

I suppose today's cheechakos are tomorrow's sourdoughs. So has the place changed? Maybe not where it counts.

# Mad About Moose!

*Alces alces gigas*, the Alaskan moose, is the largest of all moose in the world.

Healthy adult males weigh 1,200 to 1,600 pounds; females, 800 to 1,300 pounds. Twins are common. Only males produce antlers, which are at their largest when the animal is 10 to 12 years old.

Alaska adopted the moose as a state symbol—the official Land Mammal—in 1998.

The Talkeetna Historical Society sponsors the annual Moose Dropping Festival each July.

Early settlers discovered that, due to their woody nature, moose droppings make an excellent fire starter.

In December 1994, deep snow caused one city moose to scale new heights in Anchorage. Homeowner Roger Pickering called Fish and Game for help when he discovered a moose on his roof. Biologists chased it off, unhurt.

Moose biologists regularly warn Alaskans and visitors to keep their distance from moose. Do not feed them as they may become too bold toward humans. Never place yourself between a cow and her calf.

Watch out for moose! Hundreds are killed on Alaska's roadways each year.

# Go ahead and take the picture. I'm game.

Library of Congress Cataloging-in-Publication Data
    available upon request

International Standard Book Number: 0-88240-587-X

Alaska Northwest Books®
An imprint of Graphic Arts Center Publishing Company
P.O. Box 10306, Portland, Oregon 97296-0306
503-226-2402 / www.gacpc.com

Edited by Tricia Brown
Designed by Elizabeth Watson, Jean Andrews

Printed in China

## Photo Credits

Cover and title page: Danny Daniels; pages 2–3, Along the trans-Alaska pipeline, Patrick Endres; pages 4–5, Walking the tracks in Denali National Park, Thomas Sbamato; pages 6–7, Road crossing in Denali National Park, Greg Martin; pages 8–9, Grazing in Anchorage, Clark James Mishler; pages 10–11, Peeping moose in Anchorage, Julie Sprott; pages 12–13, Drive-through service in Homer, Steve Kaufman; pages 14–15, Cold day on the Kenai, Calvin W. Hall; pages 16–17, Cooling off in the kiddie pool, Anchorage, Bob Hallinen; pages 18–19, Along the highway in Southcentral, Jeff Schultz; pages 20–21, Snow dump in the city, Larry Anderson; pages 22–23, A tangle of twinkly lights, Clark James Mishler; pages 24–25, Visit to Big Game Alaska Wildlife Center, Portage Valley, Calvin W. Hall; pages 26–27, Watching out for Chitina travelers, Julie Sprott; pages 28–29, Wonder Lake smooch, Denali National Park, Gary Schultz; pages 30 and 32, Greetings from Big Game Alaska, Portage Valley, Alaska, Calvin W. Hall.